These were the days

from you to me®

from you to me®

concept by Neil Coxon

These were the days

from you to me®

This journal is for you to remember the great times you have had with your friends and colleagues.

Perfect to use when you are about to move on to pastures new . . . or simply to capture a period in your life.

Give it to the people you choose and ask them to complete their own section.

When it is finished and returned to you, this will be a record of your days together . . . a part of your life that you will treasure forever.

Hello . . .

You have been given this journal by the person detailed on the opposite page. They want to capture some great memories of the times you have spent together.

Please find the next available section and complete the questions before returning it to them. You might also want to add a photo.

This journal will be a record of the days you have spent together so please take care with your recollections and advice!

This journal belongs to . . .

A bit about the place and time we all met . . .

My name . . .

My contact details . . .

A bit about me . . .

What I thought when I first met you . . .

If I had to re-live a moment with you,
it would be . . .

My favourite memories of the times we have spent together . . .

Something I have learnt from you . . .

I wish I had said . . .

What I think you will be doing in
10 years' time?

A piece of advice for you for the future . . .

My name . . .

My contact details . . .

A bit about me . . .

What I thought when I first met you . . .

If I had to re-live a moment with you,
it would be . . .

My favourite memories of the times we have
spent together . . .

Something I have learnt from you is . . .

I wish I had said . . .

What I think you will be doing in
10 years' time?

A piece of advice for you for the future . . .

My name . . .

My contact details . . .

A bit about me . . .

What I thought when I first met you . . .

If I had to re-live a moment with you,
it would be . . .

My favourite memories of the times we have spent together . . .

Something I have learnt from you is . . .

I wish I had said . . .

What I think you will be doing in
10 years' time?

A piece of advice for you for the future . . .

My name . . .

My contact details . . .

A bit about me . . .

What I thought when I first met you . . .

If I had to re-live a moment with you,
it would be . . .

My favourite memories of the times we have spent together . . .

Something I have learnt from you is . . .

I wish I had said . . .

What I think you will be doing in
10 years' time?

A piece of advice for you for the future . . .

My name . . .

My contact details . . .

A bit about me . . .

What I thought when I first met you . . .

If I had to re-live a moment with you,
it would be . . .

My favourite memories of the times we have spent together . . .

Something I have learnt from you is . . .

I wish I had said . . .

What I think you will be doing in
10 years' time?

A piece of advice for you for the future . . .

My name . . .

My contact details . . .

A bit about me . . .

What I thought when I first met you . . .

If I had to re-live a moment with you,
it would be . . .

My favourite memories of the times we have spent together . . .

Something I have learnt from you is . . .

I wish I had said . . .

What I think you will be doing in
10 years' time?

A piece of advice for you for the future . . .

My name . . .

My contact details . . .

A bit about me . . .

What I thought when I first met you . . .

If I had to re-live a moment with you,
it would be . . .

My favourite memories of the times we have spent together . . .

Something I have learnt from you is . . .

I wish I had said . . .

What I think you will be doing in
10 years' time?

A piece of advice for you for the future . . .

My name . . .

My contact details . . .

A bit about me . . .

What I thought when I first met you . . .

If I had to re-live a moment with you,
it would be . . .

My favourite memories of the times we have spent together . . .

Something I have learnt from you is . . .

I wish I had said . . .

What I think you will be doing in
10 years' time?

A piece of advice for you for the future . . .

My name . . .

My contact details . . .

A bit about me . . .

What I thought when I first met you . . .

If I had to re-live a moment with you,
it would be . . .

My favourite memories of the times we have spent together . . .

Something I have learnt from you is . . .

I wish I had said . . .

What I think you will be doing in
10 years' time?

A piece of advice for you for the future . . .

My name . . .

My contact details . . .

A bit about me . . .

What I thought when I first met you . . .

If I had to re-live a moment with you,
it would be . . .

My favourite memories of the times we have
spent together . . .

Something I have learnt from you is . . .

I wish I had said . . .

What I think you will be doing in
10 years' time?

A piece of advice for you for the future . . .

My name . . .

My contact details . . .

A bit about me . . .

What I thought when I first met you . . .

If I had to re-live a moment with you,
it would be . . .

My favourite memories of the times we have spent together . . .

Something I have learnt from you is . . .

I wish I had said . . .

What I think you will be doing in
10 years' time?

A piece of advice for you for the future . . .

My name . . .

My contact details . . .

A bit about me . . .

What I thought when I first met you . . .

If I had to re-live a moment with you,
it would be . . .

My favourite memories of the times we have spent together . . .

Something I have learnt from you is . . .

I wish I had said . . .

What I think you will be doing in
10 years' time?

A piece of advice for you for the future . . .

My name . . .

My contact details . . .

A bit about me . . .

What I thought when I first met you . . .

If I had to re-live a moment with you,
it would be . . .

My favourite memories of the times we have
spent together . . .

Something I have learnt from you is . . .

I wish I had said . . .

What I think you will be doing in
10 years' time?

A piece of advice for you for the future . . .

My name . . .

My contact details . . .

A bit about me . . .

What I thought when I first met you . . .

If I had to re-live a moment with you,
it would be . . .

My favourite memories of the times we have spent together . . .

Something I have learnt from you is . . .

I wish I had said . . .

What I think you will be doing in
10 years' time?

A piece of advice for you for the future . . .

My name . . .

My contact details . . .

A bit about me . . .

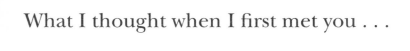

What I thought when I first met you . . .

If I had to re-live a moment with you,
it would be . . .

My favourite memories of the times we have
spent together . . .

Something I have learnt from you is . . .

I wish I had said . . .

What I think you will be doing in
10 years' time?

A piece of advice for you for the future . . .

My name . . .

My contact details . . .

A bit about me . . .

What I thought when I first met you . . .

If I had to re-live a moment with you,
it would be . . .

My favourite memories of the times we have
spent together . . .

Something I have learnt from you is . . .

I wish I had said . . .

What I think you will be doing in
10 years' time?

A piece of advice for you for the future . . .

My name . . .

My contact details . . .

A bit about me . . .

What I thought when I first met you . . .

If I had to re-live a moment with you,
it would be . . .

My favourite memories of the times we have spent together . . .

Something I have learnt from you is . . .

I wish I had said . . .

What I think you will be doing in
10 years' time?

A piece of advice for you for the future . . .

My name . . .

My contact details . . .

A bit about me . . .

What I thought when I first met you . . .

If I had to re-live a moment with you,
it would be . . .

My favourite memories of the times we have spent together . . .

Something I have learnt from you is . . .

I wish I had said . . .

What I think you will be doing in
10 years' time?

A piece of advice for you for the future . . .

My name . . .

My contact details . . .

A bit about me . . .

What I thought when I first met you . . .

If I had to re-live a moment with you,
it would be . . .

My favourite memories of the times we have spent together . . .

Something I have learnt from you is . . .

I wish I had said . . .

What I think you will be doing in
10 years' time?

A piece of advice for you for the future . . .

My name . . .

My contact details . . .

A bit about me . . .

What I thought when I first met you . . .

If I had to re-live a moment with you,
it would be . . .

My favourite memories of the times we have spent together . . .

Something I have learnt from you is . . .

I wish I had said . . .

What I think you will be doing in
10 years' time?

A piece of advice for you for the future . . .

These were the days

from you to me®

First published in the UK by *from you to me*, June 2009
Copyright, *from you to me* limited 2009
Hackless House, Murhill, Bath, BA2 7FH
www.fromyoutome.com
E-mail: hello@fromyoutome.com

ISBN 978-1-907048-13-5

Cover design by so design consultants, Wick, Bristol, UK
Printed and bound in the UK by CPI William Clowes, Beccles

This paper is manufactured from material sourced from forests certified according to strict environmental, social and economical standards.

If you liked the concept of this book, please tell your family and friends and look out for others in the *from you to me* range:

Dear Mum, from you to me   *Dear Friend, from you to me*
Dear Dad, from you to me   *Cooking up Memories, from you to me*
Dear Grandma, from you to me . *Christmas Present, Christmas Past, from you to me*
Dear Grandad, from you to me
Dear Sister, from you to me
Dear Brother, from you to me
Dear Son, from you to me   other relationship and memory journals
Dear Daughter, from you to me   available soon . . .